ITCHY SCRATCHY!

Contents

Alison Hawes

Story illustrated by
Frances Castle

Before Reading

Find out about

- Allergies and some of the things that can make you itch and sneeze!

Tricky words

- itch
- allergy
- allergic
- sneeze
- pollen
- swell
- medicine
- mild

Introduce these tricky words and help the reader when they come across them later!

Text starter

Lots of people have allergies. Does your skin ever itch? If so, you may have an allergy. Some people are allergic to pets, some are allergic to plants and some are allergic to foods.

Allergies

Do your eyes ever water?
Does your nose or your skin ever itch?
Yes?
You may have an allergy!

Pets

Some people are allergic to pets.
Their eyes and nose itch.
They sneeze a lot.

They must keep away from
these pets.

Lots of people are
allergic to cats.

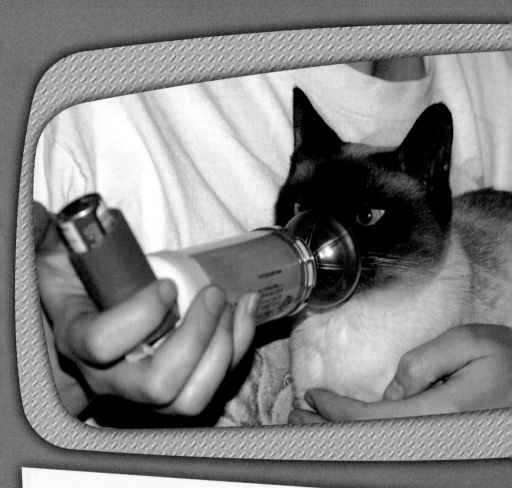

Allergic pets

Some pets are allergic to people!

Their skin may itch.

They may have a rash.

They sneeze a lot too!

Plant pollen

Some people are allergic to plant pollen.

It makes their eyes water and their nose itch.

They sneeze a lot too.

Bees

Some people are allergic to bees.
They are allergic to the bee's sting.
They may become very ill indeed.

They must keep away from bees.

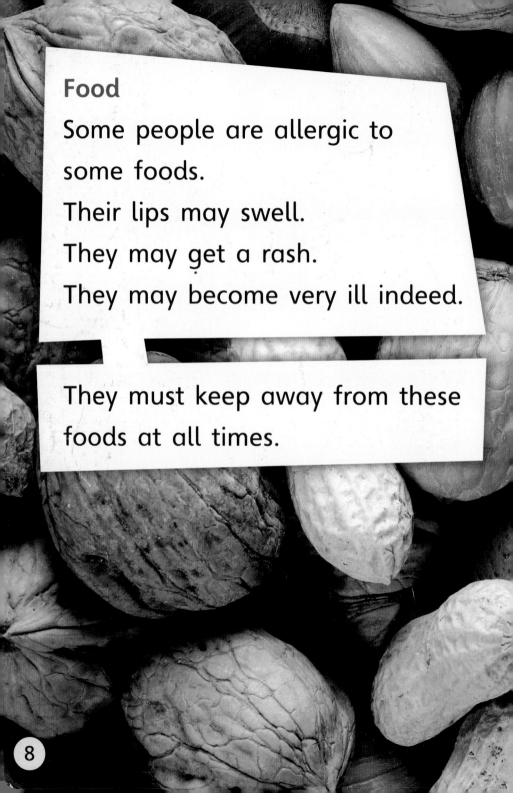

Food

Some people are allergic to some foods.

Their lips may swell.

They may get a rash.

They may become very ill indeed.

They must keep away from these foods at all times.

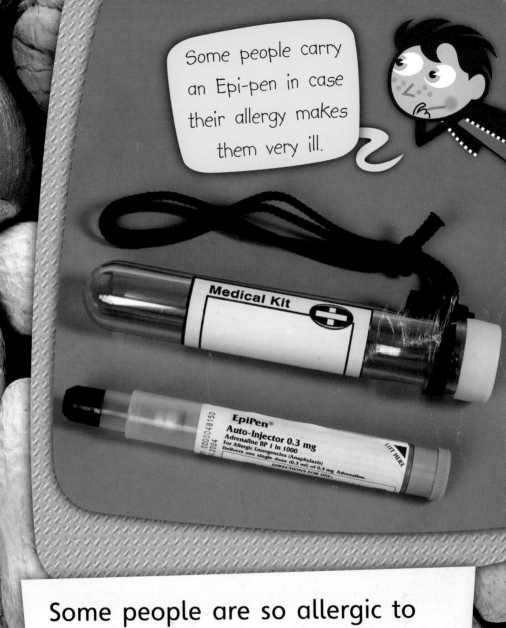

Some people carry an Epi-pen in case their allergy makes them very ill.

Some people are so allergic to some things they *must* keep medicine with them at all times.

Lots of people may have an allergy.
But for most people it will just be a mild allergy.

Atishooo!

A sneeze can travel at 160 miles an hour!

Text Detective

- What sorts of things can people be allergic to?
- Are you allergic to anything?

Word Detective

- **Phonic Focus:** Final consonant clusters
  Page 10: Sound out the four phonemes in 'most'.
  Can you blend the two sounds at the end?
- Page 9: Why is the word 'must' in bold print?
- Page 10: Find a word that rhymes with 'wild'.

Super Speller

Read these words:

from   most   must

Now try to spell them!

HA! HA! HA!

Q Why was the nose tired?

A Because it kept running!

In this story

 Max

 Tom

 Miss Bell

Tricky words

- itching powder
- laughed
- running
- bumped
- enjoy
- itched

Introduce these tricky words and help the reader when they come across them later!

Story starter

Max likes to play jokes on people. Each week he spends his pocket money at the joke shop. One day Max wanted to play a joke on his friend Tom, but Max didn't know what to buy.

12

Max
and the
Itching Powder

Max went to the joke shop.

He wanted to play a joke on Tom.

But he didn't know what to buy.

Then Max saw a big box of itching powder.

"I will buy this itching powder!" laughed Max. "This is just what I need to play a joke on Tom!"

At school, Max saw Tom's football bag.

"I will put the itching powder in Tom's football bag," said Max. "This will be the best joke *ever!*"

Then Miss Bell said, "It's time for football. Get your football bags. But *no* running!"

But Tom ran to get his
football bag!
He fell and bumped his leg.

Miss Bell looked at Tom's leg.
Tom had a big bump on his leg.

"You can't play football, Tom,"
said Miss Bell. "You need to rest
your leg."

Max looked in his football bag. "Oh no!" Max said. "My football top is not in my bag. I can't play football!"

What do you think will happen now?

"I know," said Tom, "I will lend you my football top!"

"Oh yes!" said Miss Bell.
"*Oh no!*" said Max.

Max had to put on Tom's
football top.

Max didn't enjoy playing
football that day.

He itched and itched.
He itched and itched like *mad!*

Tom laughed and laughed at Max!

Quiz

Text Detective

- Why did Tom laugh at the end of the story?
- Would you play a joke on your friends?

Word Detective

- Phonic Focus: Final consonant clusters
  Page 16: Sound out the four phonemes in 'bags'.
  Can you blend the two sounds at the end?
- Page 16: Find two small words in 'football'.
- Page 16: How many sentences are there on this page?

Super Speller

Read these words:

playing   that   bump

Now try to spell them!

HA! HA! HA!

Q What's the best way to cope with an itch?

A Start from scratch!